MW00781658

FOR NOW

# For Now

## *A Simple Reflection on Loss*

AMY JOHNSON CHONG

*Tyler Grace Chong*

Living All In, LLC.

First Printing, 2021
ISBN 9781737328209
For more information about the author as well as tools for coping with grief or walking with a loved one in times of loss, please visit www.livingallin.org.

Dedicated to all those who
have shared their stories of loss.
You have given me hope
and greater understanding.

And to my daughter, Tyler
who will undoubtedly experience
her own hope and losses.
Thank you for the honor
of being your mom.

To you, my friend...

One day you are
carefree and happy.

Full of life.

Surrounded by light

and laughter.

You love

and you are loved.

When suddenly
the earth
stops spinning.

Time

stands

still.

Everything

goes

dark.

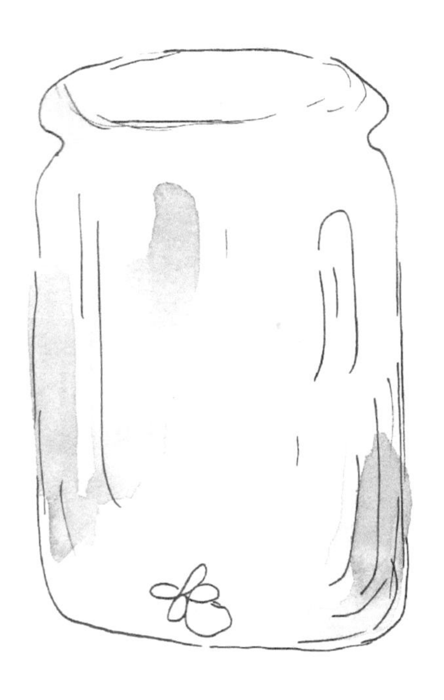

For now,

you are alone.

Except the earth

doesn't stop spinning

and you are not alone.

The sun still shines.

The people still hustle.

But for you

everything has changed.

The loss you feel
separates you.
The pain can feel
too big to hide.

And

So

You

Wait.

And wait.

And wait.

Not so much

for the wound to heal

or for the pain to subside.

But for the days to

pass.

And they do.

And in time...

it doesn't matter how much time –

you will emerge.

You will join in

the living

and the light

one day at a time.

Not unchanged.

Not forgetting.

But for now.

And that is enough.

# Reflection

CPSIA information can be obtained
at www.ICGtesting.com
Printed in the USA
LVHW071254240921
698651LV00008B/544

* 9 7 8 1 7 3 7 3 2 8 2 0 9 *